Roscoe

P.B. Bear

friends

birds

broom

scarecrow

seeds

shed

bucket

watering can

canes

string

flowerpots

pen

coat

trousers

cabbages

carrots

bird feeder

nuts

fence

Milly

A DORLING KINDERSLEY BOOK

Designers   Chris Fraser, Claire Jones
Editors   Bridget Gibbs, Deborah Murrell
DTP Designer   Jill Bunyan
Photography   Dave King
Production   Erica Rosen

First published in Great Britain in 1999 by Dorling Kindersley Limited,
9 Henrietta Street, London WC2E 8PS

www.dk.com

A CIP catalogue record for this book is available from the British Library.

ISBN 0-7513-6291-3

Colour reproduction by Colourscan
Printed in Italy by L.E.G.O

Acknowledgements
DK would like to thank Maggie Haden
and Richard Blakey for Roscoe and Milly.

Can you find the little bear in each scene?

P.B. BEAR'S
Scarecrow

Lee Davis

Early one morning,  went to visit .

It was a lovely day. The  were

singing: "TWeet, chirp, chirp, tweet."

 was in his garden. He was

pushing a  handle into the ground.

"Why are you doing that?" asked .

"I'm making a ," said , "to stop the

 eating my vegetable .

I'm using this for his body."

"Can I help?" asked .

"Yes," said  . "Come and help me look in

the for some other things to use."

On the floor of the ⬛ , the friends found

a 🪣 with a hole in the bottom and a big

ball of 🧶 . In one dark corner, 🧸 found

some long // and a 🫖 .

🐰 tripped over some 🪴 .

Clatter! Clatter! "Ouch!"

They carried all the things outside.

"We can use the to make a head

for the ," suggested .

"I think the will be better," said .

"I can draw his face with this  ."

"I'll tie on this / for his arms," said .

"He looks very thin," said  .

"I'll get him some clothes," said .

He went inside and came back with a

green  and a pair of old red .

The friends put them on the .

"These can be his hands," said .

At last, the was finished.

"Now, I can plant my ," said .

"I've got some for growing ."

"And some for , I hope," said .

"I'll hang this on the tree and fill it with these ," said . "The can eat them instead of your ."

"Do you think we have made the

scary enough?" asked .

"Let's wait to see if it works," said .

"We can hide behind the ."

The  stayed up in the tree.

Then along came into the garden.

"Ooh!" she cried, when she saw the .

and jumped up from their hiding

place. "Your scared me," giggled .

"It works!" said the friends laughing. "Now

the  can grow **and grow!**"

Roscoe

P.B. Bear

friends

birds

broom

scarecrow

seeds

shed

bucket

watering can

canes

string

flowerpots

pen

coat

trousers

cabbages

carrots

bird feeder

nuts

fence

Milly